Address Book

A directory of flowers and friends

LORENZ STATIONERY

This edition is published by Lorenz Stationery, an imprint of Anness Publishing Ltd, Hermes House,
88–89 Blackfriars Road, London SE1 8HA; tel. 020 7401 2077; fax 020 7633 9499
www.annesspublishing.com

If you like the images in this book and would like to investigate using them for publishing, promotions or advertising,
please visit our website www.practicalpictures.com for more information.

UK agent: The Manning Partnership Ltd; tel. 01225 478444; fax 01225 478440; sales@manning-partnership.co.uk
UK distributor: Book Trade Services; tel. 0116 2759086; fax 0116 2759090; uksales@booktradeservices.com;
exportsales@booktradeservices.com
North American agent/distributor: National Book Network; tel. 301 459 3366; fax 301 429 5746; www.nbnbooks.com
Australian agent/distributor: Pan Macmillan Australia; tel. 1300 135 113; fax 1300 135 103;
customer.service@macmillan.com.au
New Zealand agent/distributor: David Bateman Ltd; tel. (09) 415 7664; fax (09) 415 8892

Publisher: Joanna Lorenz
Project Editor: Fiona Eaton
Designer: Bobbie Colgate Stone
Photographers: James Duncan, Michelle Garrett, Nelson Hargreaves, Debbie Patterson
Contributors: Fiona Barnett, Kally Ellis, Tessa Evelegh, Lucinda Ganderton, Ercole Moroni,
Terence Moore, Pamela Westland

ETHICAL TRADING POLICY

Because of our ongoing ecological investment programme, you, as our customer, can have the pleasure and reassurance of
knowing that a tree is being cultivated on your behalf to naturally replace the materials used to make the book you are holding.
For further information about this scheme, go to www.annesspublishing.com/trees

© Anness Publishing Ltd 1996, 2010

All rights reserved. No part of this publication may be reproduced, stored in a retrieval system, or transmitted in
any way or by any means, electronic, mechanical, photocopying, recording or otherwise, without the
prior written permission of the copyright holder.

PUBLISHER'S NOTE

Although the advice and information in this book are believed to be accurate and true at the time of going to press, neither the
authors nor the publisher can accept any legal responsibility or liability for any errors or omissions that may be made.

Important Addresses

Name
Address

Telephone

Name
Address

Telephone

Name
Address

Telephone

Name
Address

Telephone

Name
Address

Telephone

Name
Address

Telephone

Name
Address

Telephone

Name
Address

Telephone

Name
Address

Telephone

Name
Address

Telephone

Name
Address

Telephone

Name
Address

Telephone

Name
Address

Telephone

Name
Address

Telephone

Name
Address

Telephone

These pale-stemmed roses are off-set by the moss and terracotta pot.

A

Gather ye rosebuds while ye may,
Old Time is still a-flying:
And this same flower that smiles today
To-morrow will be dying.

Robert Herrick: To the Virgins, to make much of Time

Name
Address

Telephone

Name
Address

Telephone

Name
Address

Telephone

Name
Address

Telephone

Name
Address

Telephone

Name
Address

Telephone

Name
Address

Telephone

Name
Address

Telephone

This pretty heart-shaped wreath, which is made from 40 dried red rose heads, would make an unusual and long-lasting Valentine's Day gift.

A

Name	Name	Name
Address	Address	Address
Telephone	Telephone	Telephone

Name
Address

Telephone

Name
Address

Telephone

Name
Address

Telephone

Name
Address

Telephone

Name
Address

Telephone

Name
Address

Telephone

Name
Address

Telephone

Name
Address

Telephone

Name
Address

Telephone

Name
Address

Telephone

Name
Address

Telephone

Name
Address

Telephone

Name
Address

Telephone

Apple and lavender make a quirky topiary tree.

Name
Address

Telephone

B

Kind words can be short and easy to speak, but their echoes are truly endless.
Mother Theresa

Name
Address
Telephone

Name
Address
Telephone

Name
Address
Telephone

Name
Address
Telephone

Name
Address
Telephone

Name
Address
Telephone

Name
Address
Telephone

Name
Address
Telephone

Name
Address
Telephone

Name
Address
Telephone

Name
Address
Telephone

Name
Address
Telephone

Name
Address
Telephone

Name
Address
Telephone

A pomander of dried rose heads will give off a gentle aroma.

B

Name
Address

Telephone

Name
Address

Telephone

Name
Address

Telephone

Name
Address

Telephone

Name
Address

Telephone

Name
Address

Telephone

Name
Address

Telephone

Name
Name

Name

Name
Address

Telephone

This posy is for a special friend, with lavender meaning "devoted attention" and pink roses denoting "affection" or "love" in the language of flowers.

1 Use small bunches of lavender to create the basic structure and shape of the posy.

2 Push single rosebuds into the lavender, spacing them evenly.

3 Edge the posy with wired leaves. Unravel a paper ribbon and use to cover the wire and stalks. Finish off by tying the ends of the ribbon into a bow.

Name	*Name*	*Name*
Address	*Address*	*Address*
Telephone	*Telephone*	*Telephone*
Name	*Name*	*Name*
Address	*Address*	*Address*
Telephone	*Telephone*	*Telephone*
Name	*Name*	
Address	*Address*	
Telephone	*Telephone*	

Dried deep pink peonies and small blue globe thistles are massed tightly around a candle in a terracotta flowerpot, secured in plastic foam for dried flowers.

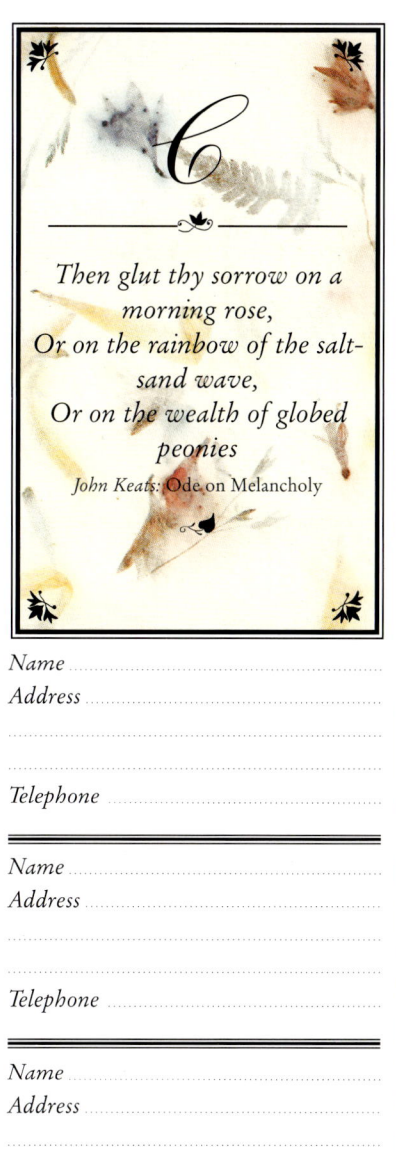

Then glut thy sorrow on a morning rose,
Or on the rainbow of the salt-sand wave,
Or on the wealth of globed peonies

John Keats: Ode on Melancholy

Name
Address

Telephone

Name
Address

Telephone

Name
Address

Telephone

Name
Address

Telephone

Name
Address

Telephone

Name
Address

Telephone

Name
Address

Telephone

Name
Address

Telephone

Name
Address

Telephone

Name
Address

Telephone

Name
Address

Telephone

A still life of scabious and anemones is most appealing.

C

Name	Name	Name
Address	Address	Address
Telephone	Telephone	Telephone

Name	Name	Name
Address	Address	Address
Telephone	Telephone	Telephone

Name	Name	Name
Address	Address	Address
Telephone	Telephone	Telephone

The soft pastel colours give this trug basket a summery appeal and the starfish evoke images of the sea, making it a delightful bathroom display.

1 Fit a block of plastic foam for dried flowers into a trug basket and create the overall domed shape of the arrangement using 50 natural phalaris stems.

2 Add 40 shell pink rose stems and 20 cream strawflowers, recessing some flowers to give depth. Arrange 100 lavender heads, in groups of five, among the other flowers.

3 Double leg mount 15 small dried starfish on stub (floral) wires and distribute them evenly throughout the display.

D

Name
Address

Telephone

Name
Address

Telephone

Name
Address

Telephone

D

If Jove would give the leafy bowers
A queen for all their world of flowers
The rose would be the choice of Jove,
And blush the queen of every grove.

Sappho

Name
Address

Telephone

Name
Address

Telephone

Name
Address

Telephone

Name
Address

Telephone

Name
Address

Telephone

Name
Address

Telephone

Name
Address

Telephone

Multi-layered tulip heads are massed in a topiary tree.

D

Roses, eucalyptus and scabious, gathered from the garden, are tied in a simple posy, wrapped in brown paper and finished off with a pretty ribbon bow.

Name
Address

Telephone

Name
Address

Telephone

Name
Address

Telephone

Name
Address

Telephone

Name
Address

Telephone

Name
Address

Telephone

D

Name
Address

Telephone

Name
Address

Telephone

Name
Address

Telephone

Name
Address

Telephone

Name
Address

Telephone

Mistletoe and winterberry are tied on to a twisted cane ring with twine to make a traditional kissing ring. Checked ribbons are used to hang the finished ring.

E

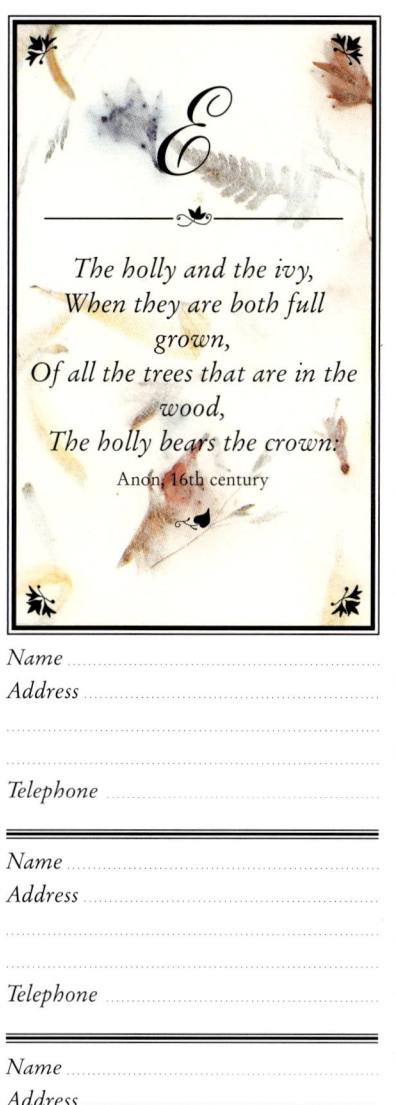

*The holly and the ivy,
When they are both full grown,
Of all the trees that are in the wood,
The holly bears the crown:*

Anon, 16th century

Name
Address

Telephone

Name
Address

Telephone

Name
Address

Telephone

Name
Address

Telephone

Name
Address

Telephone

Name
Address

Telephone

Name
Address

Telephone

Name
Address

Telephone

Name
Address

Telephone

Name
Address

Telephone

Name
Address

Telephone

Name
Address

Telephone

Name
Address

Telephone

Name
Address

Telephone

Simply mixing three or four types of foliage can be very effective.

E

| Name |
| Address |
| Telephone |

| Name |
| Address |
| Telephone |

| Name |
| Address |
| Telephone |

| Name |
| Address |
| Telephone |

| Name |
| Address |
| Telephone |

| Name |
| Address |
| Telephone |

| Name |
| Address |
| Telephone |

An aromatic, culinary topiary is set in a toning flowerpot.

| Name |
| Address |
| Telephone |

| Name |
| Address |
| Telephone |

| Name |
| Address |
| Telephone |

| Name |
| Address |
| Telephone |

| Name |
| Address |
| Telephone |

This star-shaped wall decoration is made of cinnamon sticks and is embellished with lavender. A delightful aromatic mix of flowers and spices will fill the air.

Name
Address

Telephone

Name
Address

Telephone

Name
Address

Telephone

Name
Address

Telephone

Lavenders blue, dilly dilly
Lavenders green
When I am king, dilly dilly
You shall be queen
Traditional song

Name
Address

Telephone

Name
Address

Telephone

Name
Address

Telephone

Name
Address

Telephone

Name
Address

Telephone

Name
Address

Telephone

Name
Address

Telephone

A delicate rose and its own foliage ensures an elegant corsage.

This romantic pot-pourri is made of rosebuds, lavender and moss. Perfume the pot-pourri by drizzling your favourite essential oil over the moss.

Name	Name	Name
Address	Address	Address
Telephone	Telephone	Telephone

Name	Name	
Address	Address	Red roses link these two jewel-like pots visually: contrasting with lime green 'Santini' chrysanthemums in one and combining with purple phlox in the other.
Telephone	Telephone	

Wired starfish create a frame for massed shell pink dried rose heads in this beautiful bedroom wreath. Space is left in the design for a hanging ribbon.

Name ....
Address ....
....
Telephone ....

Name ....
Address ....
....
Telephone ....

Name ....
Address ....
....
Telephone ....

Name ....
Address ....
....
Telephone ....

Name ....
Address ....
....
Telephone ....

G

When a friend asks, there is no tomorrow.
17th-century proverb

Name
Address

Telephone

Name
Address

Telephone

Name
Address

Telephone

Name
Address

Telephone

Name
Address

Telephone

Name
Address

Telephone

Name
Address

Telephone

Name
Address

Telephone

Name
Address

Telephone

Name
Address

Telephone

Name
Address

Telephone

Name
Address

Telephone

Name
Address

Telephone

A festive Easter display of tulips and colourful painted eggs.

G

| Name |
| Address |
| |
| Telephone |

| Name |
| Address |
| |
| Telephone |

| Name |
| Address |
| |
| Telephone |

| Name |
| Address |
| |
| Telephone |

| Name |
| Address |
| |
| Telephone |

| Name |
| Address |
| |
| Telephone |

| Name |
| Address |
| |
| Telephone |

| Name |
| Address |
| |
| Telephone |

| Name |
| Address |
| |
| Telephone |

| Name |
| Address |
| |
| Telephone |

Contorted hazel twigs give support to the bright yellow sunflowers.

| Name |
| Address |
| |
| Telephone |

| Name |
| Address |
| |
| Telephone |

| Name |
| Address |
| |
| Telephone |

H I

Name
Address

Telephone

Name
Address

Telephone

Name
Address

Telephone

Name
Address

Telephone

*Then give the world the best that you have
And the best will come back to you.*

Madeline Bridges

Name
Address

Telephone

Name
Address

Telephone

Name
Address

Telephone

Name
Address

Telephone

Name
Address

Telephone

Name
Address

Telephone

Name
Address

Telephone

A fruity tree for the kitchen of beech leaves and preserved pears.

A change from mistletoe and holly at Christmas is provided by this 30 cm (12 in) wreath which incorporates wired clementines, pyracanthus and ivy leaves.

H I

Name	Name	Name
Address	Address	Address
Telephone	Telephone	Telephone
Name	Name	Name
Address	Address	Address
Telephone	Telephone	Telephone
Name	Name	Name
Address	Address	Address
Telephone	Telephone	Telephone

This delightful arrangement combining forest fruits and rosehips with garden anemones becomes a sumptuous display when placed in an elegant vase.

1 Fill your chosen vase with water and use blackberry stems to establish the outline shape. Add rosehips to create a visual balance (strip the thorns from the stems first).

2 Add white Japanese anemones (these are 'Honorine Jobert') throughout the arrangement. Take particular care when handling these delicate flowers.

3 Add the vine leaves to the arrangement so that they form a collar around the base of the vase.

Name
Address

Telephone

Name
Address

Telephone

Name
Address

Telephone

Always choose fresh flowers that reflect your style and personality.

JK

Oh my luve's like a red, red rose,
That's newly sprung in June;
Oh my luve's like a melodie
That's sweetly played in tune.

Robert Burns: A Red, Red Rose

Name
Address

Telephone

Name
Address

Telephone

Name
Address

Telephone

Name
Address

Telephone

Name
Address

Telephone

Name
Address

Telephone

Name
Address

Telephone

Name
Address

Telephone

To create these sophisticated napkin decorations, suitable for a wedding reception, wrap an ivy trail around a napkin, then make a hand-spiralled, flat-backed sheaf using four or five lily-of-the-valley stems, and three cyclamen flowers and leaves. Tie with gold cord then position on the ivy and secure in place with the cord.

Name	Name ....
Address	Address ....
....	....
....	....
Telephone	Telephone ....
Name	Name ....
Address	Address ....
....	....
....	....
Telephone	Telephone ....

JK

Name	Name	Name
Address	Address	Address
Telephone	Telephone	Telephone

Name	Name	
Address	Address	This ring is strongly evocative of the seaside. Mussel shells are glued to the plastic foam ring and globe thistles are pushed into the foam to fill the gaps.
Telephone	Telephone	

L

Friendships multiply joys and divide griefs.
19th-century proverb

Name
Address

Telephone

Name
Address

Telephone

Name
Address

Telephone

Name
Address

Telephone

Name
Address

Telephone

Name
Address

Telephone

Name
Address

Telephone

Name
Address

Telephone

Name
Address

Telephone

Name
Address

Telephone

Name
Address

Telephone

Name
Address

Telephone

Name
Address

Telephone

Name
Address

Telephone

Bold shapes and colours give this display a contemporary feel.

L

Classical urns lend dried-flower arrangements a timeless feel.

Name
Address

Telephone

Name
Address

Telephone

Name
Address

Telephone

Name
Address

Telephone

Name
Address

Telephone

Name
Address

Telephone

Name
Address

Telephone

Name
Address

Telephone

Name
Address

Telephone

Name
Address

Telephone

Name
Address

Telephone

Name
Address

Telephone

Name
Address

Telephone

An audacious combination of orange roses set against vivid purple anemones and metallic blue berries of laurustinus makes a vibrant Christmas display.

| Name |
| Address |
| |
| Telephone |

| Name |
| Address |
| |
| Telephone |

A fresh herbal wreath makes an ideal gift for an enthusiastic cook.

| Name |
| Address |
| |
| Telephone |

| Name |
| Address |
| |
| Telephone |

M

The rainbow comes and goes,
And lovely is the rose;

William Wordsworth: Ode Intimations of Immortality

| Name |
| Address |
| |
| Telephone |

| Name |
| Address |
| |
| Telephone |

| Name |
| Address |
| |
| Telephone |

| Name |
| Address |
| |
| Telephone |

| Name |
| Address |
| |
| Telephone |

| Name |
| Address |
| |
| Telephone |

| Name |
| Address |
| |
| Telephone |

This welcoming wreath is made with pliable buddleia branches. Trailing ivy and red berries are entwined around the heart and a white rose completes the design.

Massed dried flowers never fail to create an impressive display.

Name	Name	Name
Address	Address	Address
Telephone	Telephone	Telephone
Name	Name	Name
Address	Address	Address
Telephone	Telephone	Telephone
Name	Name	Name
Address	Address	Address
Telephone	Telephone	Telephone
Name	Name	Name
Address	Address	Address
Telephone	Telephone	Telephone
Name	Name	Name
Address	Address	Address
Telephone	Telephone	Telephone

N

Beauty, strength, youth, are flowers but fading seen; Duty, faith, love, are roots and ever green.

George Peel: A Farewell to Arms

Name
Address

Telephone

Name
Address

Telephone

Name
Address

Telephone

Name
Address

Telephone

Name
Address

Telephone

Name
Address

Telephone

Name
Address

Telephone

Name
Address

Telephone

Name
Address

Telephone

Name
Address

Telephone

Name
Address

Telephone

Name
Address

Telephone

Name
Address

Telephone

This flower-edged basket with a candle makes a lovely gift.

N

Name
Address

Telephone

Name
Address

Telephone

Name
Address

Telephone

Name
Address

Telephone

Name
Address

Telephone

Name
Address

Telephone

Name
Address

Telephone

Name
Address

Telephone

Tussie mussies make perfect gifts or small table centrepieces. One features blackberry stems and Japanese anemones; the other delphiniums and rosehip stems.

These arrangements are ideal for young bridesmaids. The birch leaves, yellow roses and fennel are secured in plastic foam. A raffia bow completes the design.

Name ....
Address ....
....
Telephone ....

Name ....
Address ....
....
Telephone ....

Name ....
Address ....
....
Telephone ....

Name ....
Address ....
....
Telephone ....

Name ....
Address ....
....
Telephone ....

O

The best way to make children good is to make them happy.
Oscar Wilde

Name
Address

Telephone

Name
Address

Telephone

Name
Address

Telephone

Name
Address

Telephone

To straighten stems, wrap them in newspaper and stand in cool water.

Name
Address

Telephone

Name
Address

Telephone

Name
Address

Telephone

Name
Address

Telephone

Name
Address

Telephone

Name
Address

Telephone

Name
Address

Telephone

Name
Address

Telephone

Name
Address

Telephone

Name	Name	Name ....
Address	Address	Address ....
....	....	....
Telephone	Telephone	Telephone ....

	Name	Name ....
Cheerful pink and yellow "mini-gerbera", simply pushed into plastic foam in enamel mugs, form a naive, colourful group that children will love.	Address	Address ....
	....	....
	Telephone	Telephone ....

P Q

Name
Address

Telephone

Name
Address

Telephone

Name
Address

Telephone

Fabric, flowerpots and dried flowers make up this pretty swag.

*In the last month of May
I made her posies;
I heard her often say
That she loved roses*

Anon: Phillada Flouts Me

Name
Address

Telephone

Name
Address

Telephone

Name
Address

Telephone

Name
Address

Telephone

Name
Address

Telephone

Name
Address

Telephone

Name
Address

Telephone

Name
Address

Telephone

In Elizabethan times pomanders were filled with herbs or flowers and carried to perfume the air. Today they are more likely to be a bridesmaid's accessory.

Name	Name	Name
Address	Address	Address
Telephone	Telephone	Telephone

Name	Name	Name
Address	Address	Address
Telephone	Telephone	Telephone

Name	Name	Name
Address	Address	Address
Telephone	Telephone	Telephone

This delicate arrangement in a practical container is an ideal gift for parents on the birth of a baby.

1 Wedge some soaked plastic foam into a small, galvanized bucket and use a bunch of *Pittosporum* to create the domed outline.

2 Distribute 15 pale pink tulips (these are 'Angelique') throughout the foliage then add five stems of white spray roses, with buds at the outside and full blooms in the centre.

3 Add 10 stems each of white ranunculus and phlox and finally add lavender, in groups of three, evenly throughout the flowers and foliage. Tie a patterned ribbon around the bucket and finish in a generous bow.

R

It is astonishing how short a time it takes for wonderful things to happen.
Frances Hodgson Burnett

Larkspur, roses and hydrangea are tiered in a round basket.

Name		
Address		
Telephone		

Tiered baskets are very effective and one of the easiest displays for a beginner. For a dramatic display, ensure that each layer of flowers is the correct height.

Name
Address

Telephone

Name
Address

Telephone

Name	
Address	
Telephone	

Name	
Address	
Telephone	

Name	
Address	
Telephone	

Name	
Address	
Telephone	

A collection of these delightful dried-flower pew ends produces a dramatic effect in church. The candle is taped between two canes and dried pink larkspur and roses conceal the fixing. The flowers are secured with stub (floral) wires and tied with a large raffia bow. A strong S-shaped wire is attached to the back for hanging.

| Name |
| Address |
| |
| Telephone |

| Name |
| Address |
| |
| Telephone |

| Name |
| Address |
| |
| Telephone |

| Name |
| Address |
| |
| Telephone |

| Name |
| Address |
| |
| Telephone |

| Name |
| Address |
| |
| Telephone |

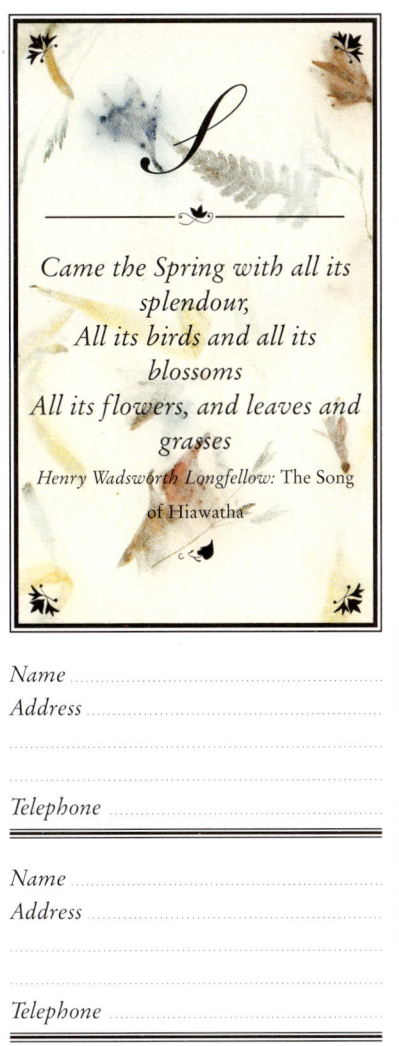

Came the Spring with all its splendour,
All its birds and all its blossoms
All its flowers, and leaves and grasses
Henry Wadsworth Longfellow: The Song of Hiawatha

| Name |
| Address |
| |
| Telephone |

| Name |
| Address |
| |
| Telephone |

| Name |
| Address |
| |
| Telephone |

| Name |
| Address |
| |
| Telephone |

| Name |
| Address |
| |
| Telephone |

| Name |
| Address |
| |
| Telephone |

A cinnamon covered Advent candle burns down to Christmas.

S

Nuts and fir cones combine in a garland trimmed with a bow.

Name
Address

Telephone

Name
Address

Telephone

Name
Address

Telephone

Name
Address

Telephone

Name
Address

Telephone

Name
Address

Telephone

Name
Address

Telephone

Name
Address

Telephone

Name
Address

Telephone

Name
Address

Telephone

Name
Address

Telephone

Name
Address

Telephone

An old picture frame is used as the base of this love-and-kisses collage. Crossed cinnamon sticks make the "kisses" while tropical seedheads are the hearts.

Name
Address

Telephone

Name
Address

Telephone

Name
Address

Telephone

Friends tie their purses with a cobweb thread.
19th-century proverb

Name
Address

Telephone

Name
Address

Telephone

Name
Address

Telephone

Name
Address

Telephone

Name
Address

Telephone

A flower stack brings welcome warmth and colour to a room.

Name
Address

Telephone

Name
Address

Telephone

Name
Address

Telephone

Name
Address

Telephone

Name
Address

Telephone

Name
Address

Telephone

Name
Address

Telephone

Name
Address

Telephone

Name
Address

Telephone

The bright reds, yellows and green on the olive oil tin make it an attractive container for this arrangement of 40 dried 'Jacaranda' roses.

T

Name	Name	Name
Address	Address	Address
Telephone	Telephone	Telephone

Name	Name	Name
Address	Address	Address
Telephone	Telephone	Telephone

Name	Name	Name
Address	Address	Address
Telephone	Telephone	Telephone

This wreath will fill any room with the rich scent of summer lavender.

1 Tie a length of natural rope to a 30 cm (12 in) diameter twig wreath.

2 Hold a bunch of lavender across the wreath with the flowers pointing outwards. Wind the rope around the stems, then over the wreath, and spiral bind the stems in place.

3 Place a second lavender bunch to the right of the first; bind in place. Continue to spiral bind bunches until the wreath is covered. Tie off the rope securely and finish off with a loop for hanging.

UVW

Name
Address

Telephone

Name
Address

Telephone

Name
Address

Telephone

Name
Address

Telephone

Come in the evening, or come in the morning
Come when you're looked for, or come without warning
Thomas Davis: The Welcome

Name
Address

Telephone

Name
Address

Telephone

Name
Address

Telephone

Name
Address

Telephone

Name
Address

Telephone

Name
Address

Telephone

Name
Address

Telephone

Grouping displays of simple flowers can increase their impact.

Golden pompon dahlias have long, straight stems which makes them easy to arrange in a large display. Here they are supported by campanula and rosehips.

U V W

| Name |
| Address |
| |
| Telephone |

| Name |
| Address |
| |
| Telephone |

| Name |
| Address |
| |
| Telephone |

Pressed flowers make lovely personalized greetings cards.

| Name |
| Address |
| |
| Telephone |

| Name |
| Address |
| |
| Telephone |

| Name |
| Address |
| |
| Telephone |

| Name |
| Address |
| |
| Telephone |

| Name |
| Address |
| |
| Telephone |

| Name |
| Address |
| |
| Telephone |

| Name |
| Address |
| |
| Telephone |

| Name |
| Address |
| |
| Telephone |

Personalize a gift to a special friend by using handmade paper scattered with pressed flowers. Secure with twine and tuck three dried red roses underneath.

XYZ

Name
Address

Telephone

Name
Address

Telephone

Name
Address

Telephone

XYZ

The red rose cries, 'She is near, she is near'
And the white rose weeps, 'She is late';
The larkspur listens, 'I hear, I hear'
And the lily whispers, 'I wait'.

Alfred, Lord Tennyson: Maud

Name
Address

Telephone

Name
Address

Telephone

Name
Address

Telephone

This simple fireplace display should be turned occasionally when *in situ* so that it fades evenly.

1 Put some scrunched-up chicken wire in the basket. You will need one bunch each of amaranthus, pink larkspur, pink roses, red roses and lavender for the design.

2 Push individual stems of amaranthus through the wire mesh to the bottom of the basket. Add stems of larkspur, distributing them evenly.

3 Add the roses and lavender, placing some rose heads low down for added interest. Check that the balance of the design is correct from all angles.

XYZ

Name
Address

Telephone

Name
Address

Telephone

Name
Address

Telephone

Name
Address

Telephone

Name
Address

Telephone

Name
Address

Telephone

Name
Address

Telephone

Name
Address

Telephone

Pale pink roses and peonies give a summery, soft look to this fireplace arrangement and the logs and raffia bow give the display a countryside feel.